The tickle

It's fun when Dad tickles me—I giggle.
I giggle when Mum tickles me, too.
But when my sister tickles me,
   what happens?
I don't giggle. I just get cross!

What happens to the rain?

Raindrops patter on my roof.
What happens to the rain?
It dribbles from the gutter, then
    it trickles down the drain.

It swirls down pipes, then into streams,
As swift as swift can be,
Then it swirls into the rivers as
    they sweep down to the sea.

The beetles' ball

With a toot on the flute, with
a twiddle on the fiddle,
Let's all go to the beetles' ball.

See the ants in a ring with
   the weevils in the middle.
They all skip to the may bug's call.

5

It's a spree, you can see, as
the crickets chirp and chatter.
A spider bangs on a big bass drum.

6

See the moths twist and twirl.
Hear the earwigs clitter-clatter.
While the bees clap hands and
   the hornets hum.

7

See the grasshoppers hop.
How the termites jig and jitter!
The bumble bees sing a beetles' tune.

8

All the birds sit on twigs in
the trees and twitter-twitter.
And the hornet plays a cornet at
the beetles' ball in June.

the end

9

The ice giants

There was once a land of ice where the
  ice giants lived in a silver palace.
The land of ice was a place where no-one
  had ever been.
The giants lived there in peace.

There was a legend about the giants.
It was said they had a huge treasure.
They kept the treasure all over the palace.
But since no-one could get to it, there
   was no danger that it would be stolen.

11

Then some men crossed the land of ice to
   look for the ice palace.
They wanted to steal the treasure from
   the gentle ice giants.
At last they found the place.

The ice giants had never seen men before.
'Come in,' they said, 'You are welcome.'
'What a strange place!' said the men.
One of them picked up a bracelet, and
one of them held up a necklace.

'We want your treasure,' said a man.
He lit a torch and held it out.
The ice giants had never seen a flame, and
   they shrank back in fear.
The men took all the treasure they could.

Once the men were home, they gave a
 little dance round the box of treasure.
'It's nice to be rich,' said one of them.
Then they looked in the box and gasped.
The box was full of water.

Me first

A hedgehog and a badger once met on
   a bridge over a gorge.
They could not get past each other.
'Budge,' said the badger. 'Me first.'
'And why should I budge?' said
   the hedgehog.

'I'm bigger than you,' said the badger.
Nearby, a goat stood on a ledge of
the gorge.
They asked her to judge the matter.
'One of you must stop still and let the
better one climb over,' she said.

17

'I'm the better one,' said the badger.
He began to climb over at once, but
    the hedgehog's prickles were sharp.
'Ouch!' yelped the badger, and he fell
    over the edge into the water.

'Ha, ha, ha!' chuckled the hedgehog. 'That
    will teach you.'
He chuckled so much that he fell over
    the edge of the bridge too.
'That will teach them both,' said the goat.

'Oh Dad!'

Mr Brown was out on his lawn when his son
ran up and said, 'Oh Dad, it's awful.'
'I just saw something run downstairs and
out of our door.
It had no legs!'

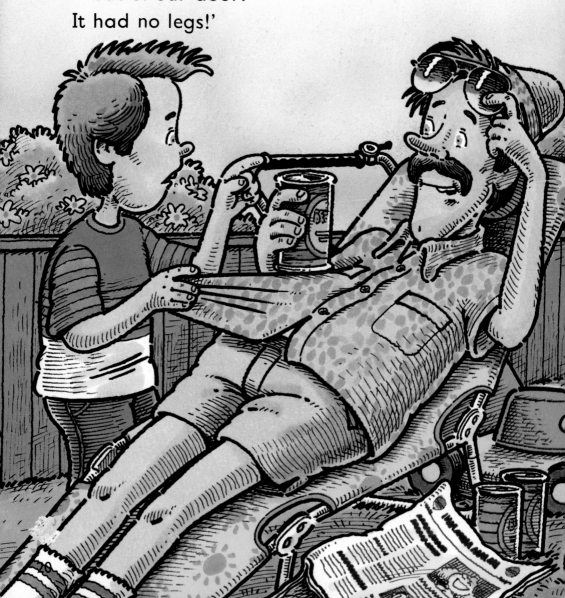

Mr Brown gave a yawn.
'Now how can that be?' he asked.
'What can run down our stairs and
out of the door with no legs?'
'Water,' shouted the little boy.

Our dog

Our dog's a soppy dog,
   a silly dog, a floppy dog.
Our dog's a lazy dog,
   a chasing, racing, crazy dog.
Our dog's a happy dog,
   he's not a mean or snappy dog.

Our dog's a wise dog,
   a 'look you in the eyes' dog.
Our dog's a grand dog,
   a loving, 'lick your hand' dog.
Our dog's a rare dog,
   a sleepy, 'time to spare' dog.

Our dog is our dog,
  a full of grins and smiles, dog.
You'd have to go for miles and miles to
  find a dog like our dog.